THE UNBELIEVABLE GWENPOOL #7 VARIANT
BY CARLY MONARDO

THE UNBELIEVABLE GWENPOOL #5
MARVEL TSUM TSUM TAKEOVER VARIANT
BY EMANUELA LUPACCHINO & JASON KEITH

WELP...

--I JUST WANTED TO KEEP THE PEACE. PLEASE DON'T MAKE THIS ABOUT ME.

HA.

WELL.

GOOD FOR YOU.

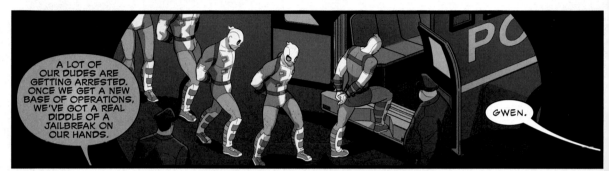

A LOT OF OUR DUDES ARE GETTING ARRESTED. ONCE WE GET A NEW BASE OF OPERATIONS, WE'VE GOT A REAL DIDDLE OF A JAILBREAK ON OUR HANDS.

GWEN.

WHAT?

NO, GWEN. THERE WILL BE NO JAILBREAK.

NO, I THINK I CAN WORK SOMETHING OUT. SEE, ONE OF US CAN GET A MAP OF THE JAIL TATTOOED--

EVERYTHING WAS IN THAT BASE. AND IT'S GONE.

I DO NOT NEED TO CONSULT THE SPIRITS TO KNOW OUR CLIENT WILL NOT HIRE US AGAIN.

IT IS TIME TO DISSOLVE.

UNDER M.O.D.O.K.'S LEADERSHIP, WE WERE PROFITABLE, AND WE DID NOT CREATE UNDUE TROUBLE.

NOW, WE BARELY ESCAPED DEATH, ARE CURRENTLY HUNTED BY THE POLICE...

...AND BROKE.

ALL RIGHT, LOOKS LIKE IT'S SAFE TO SEND IN YOUR GUYS NOW.

THANKS, POOLE. I CAN'T SAY THIS OFFICIALLY ON BEHALF OF THE NYPD, BUT...

...I APPRECIATE YOU GIVING US THE OPPORTUNITY TO WARN PEOPLE TO EVACUATE.

BILL, I FOUND YOUR PHONE! LOOKS LIKE YOU HAVE SOME MISSED CALLS.

SIR! WHAT'S YOUR NAME?

WHAT? WHY ARE YOU ASKING?

SIR, YOU JUST *SAVED* THIS NEIGHBORHOOD FROM AN *ALIEN* ATTACK!

I--

ARE YOU A *CYBORG*, SIR?

FROM PART OF YOUR FACE, YOU APPEAR TO BE A *DOOMBOT*.

NO, PLEASE--

BLAM BLAM BLAM

HA HA! OH, HAVING A PERSONAL ARMY IS *NICE!* IT'S *REAAAAL* NICE!

AWESOME.

OKAY, BACK TO FOCUSING ON THE--

WWMMMMMMM

--SHIPS.

NEIGHBORS? NO ONE'S HERE...

OKAY, THEN. NO NEED TO GET CRUSHED, MYSELF! GET OUT! CHECK THE OTHER HOUSES!

WOMP WOMP WOMP

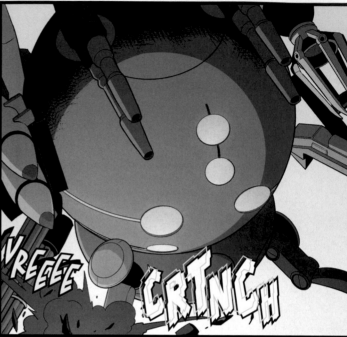

VREEEE

CRTNCH

CECIL, WE GOTTA DO SOMETHING ABOUT THE LITTLE GUYS!

THEY'RE ALL TOO CLOSE FOR OUR WEAPONS.

'KAY...

RONNIE, YOU READY DOWN THERE YET?

JUST FINISHED, GWEN. BUT AGAIN, I DO NOT SEE POINT.

BECAUSE THIS MOMENT WON'T WORK IF IT'S JUST GENERIC HENCHMEN.

STOP!

WHAT THE HEY NOW IS THIS?

IT'S KREE. I'VE SEEN IT BEFORE.

ARE YOU SURE? I THINK THAT'S VINNIE DOONAN UP IN THE SKY THERE...

I'M PRETTY SURE VINNIE DOONAN'S NO KREE, SAMANTHA.

HRM.

THIS WAS *NEVER* MEANT TO ESCALATE TO THIS POINT! *ESPECIALLY* NOT *HERE*, OF ALL PLACES, DAMN IT!

YOU BACKED THE WRONG HORSE, BABY. NOW IT'S *PERSONAL*.

GWEN, YOU STILL DON'T KNOW HOW TO USE THIS.

GET THE TEUTHIDANS TO RELEASE GWEN POOLE'S AMAZING FRIENDS, AND THEN WE CAN GO HAVE THIS FIGHT IN THE OCEAN OR SOMEPLACE WHERE IT WON'T BOTHER YOU.

TEUTHIDANS, PLEASE, I JUST DON'T WANT ANY VIOLENCE *HERE*. YOU CAN STILL KILL HER, YOU KNOW THAT. JUST DO WHAT SHE ASKS FOR NOW.

OH, *VERY* CLASSY, MONSIEUR. YOU ARE NOW TRULY ZE WORST BOSS I HAVE EVER HAD.

QUIET, BATROC.

...AND I FREELANCE FOR *HYDRA*.

IT'S GETTING TO BE ABOUT LUNCHTIME. WHAT WERE YOU THINKING?

OH, I DON'T KNOW. LEFTOVER SITUATION'S PRETTY DICEY, I IMAGINE.

WELL, YOU *COULD* STICK THE LAST COUPLE CHUNKS OF THAT GENERAL TSO'S CHICKEN INTO SOME EGGS AND SCRAMBLE IT UP, BUT, UH...

MIXING CHICKEN MEAT WITH CHICKEN EGGS SEEMS LIKE TAUNTING GOD.

HM. I WAS GOING TO SAY IT MIGHT JUST BE GROSS.

WE COULD ORDER TACOS?

OOH! TACOS! I CO--

CRUNCH

WHAT THE HECK WAS THAT?

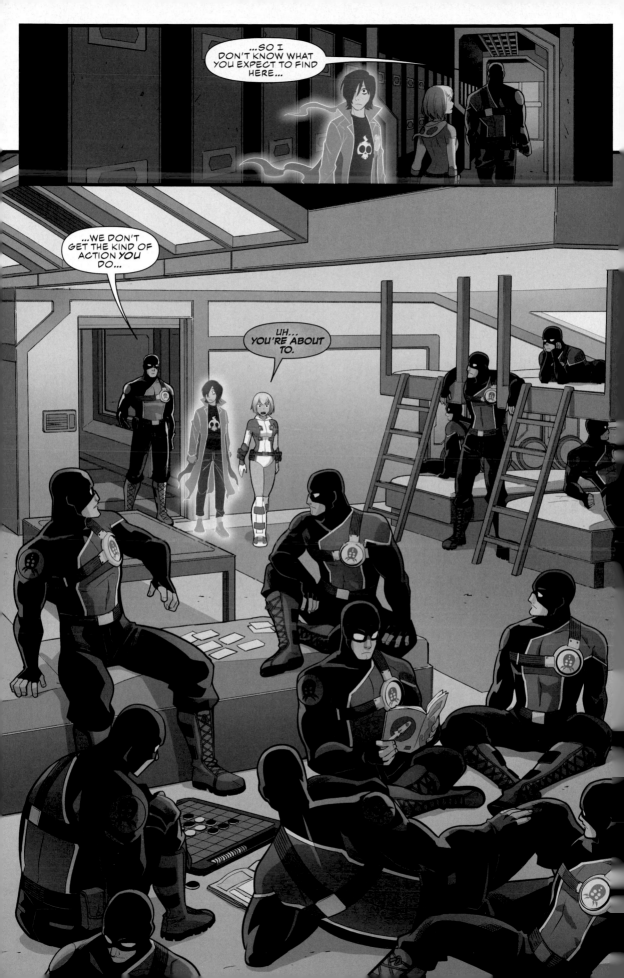

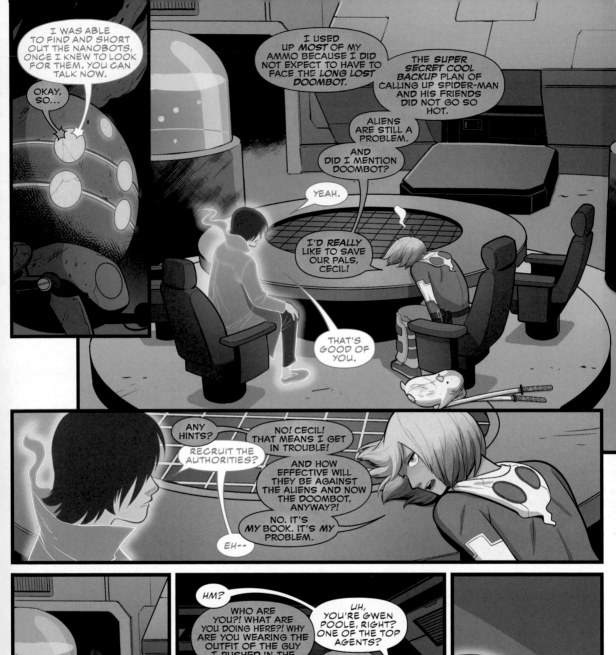

I WAS ABLE TO FIND AND SHORT OUT THE NANOBOTS, ONCE I KNEW TO LOOK FOR THEM. YOU CAN TALK NOW.

OKAY, SO...

I USED UP *MOST* OF MY AMMO BECAUSE I DID NOT EXPECT TO HAVE TO FACE THE *LONG LOST* DOOMBOT.

THE *SUPER SECRET COOL BACKUP* PLAN OF CALLING UP SPIDER-MAN AND HIS FRIENDS DID NOT GO SO HOT.

ALIENS ARE STILL A PROBLEM.

AND DID I MENTION DOOMBOT?

YEAH.

I'D *REALLY* LIKE TO SAVE OUR PALS, CECIL!

THAT'S GOOD OF YOU.

ANY HINTS?

RECRUIT THE AUTHORITIES?

NO! CECIL! THAT MEANS I GET IN TROUBLE!

AND HOW EFFECTIVE WILL THEY BE AGAINST THE ALIENS AND NOW THE DOOMBOT, ANYWAY?!

NO. IT'S *MY* BOOK. IT'S *MY* PROBLEM.

EH--

WAH! WHO IS THAT?!

HM?

WHO ARE YOU?! WHAT ARE YOU DOING HERE?! WHY ARE YOU WEARING THE OUTFIT OF THE GUY I PUSHED IN THE FIRE?!

UH, YOU'RE GWEN POOLE, RIGHT? ONE OF THE TOP AGENTS?

TOP AGENTS?

YEAH, YOU KNOW THE ONES M.O.D.O.K. SENDS ON ALL THE MISSIONS?

WHERE *IS* M.O.D.O.K., BY THE WAY? OUR LAST PAYCHECK IS LATE, AND JUST BECAUSE HE'S NOT SENDING US OUT DOESN'T MEAN WE'RE OFF PAYROLL.

I HATE DOING THIS! WHERE ARE YOU, GWENPOOL?!

YEAH, SO, THAT'S A *DOOMBOT*.

MAYBE *PRIORITIZE*?

EH...

WHAT'S YOUR NAME?

IT'S OFFICER GRAY.

GREAT. OFFICER GRAY, YOU ARE NOW NO LONGER AN EXTRA TO ME, AND BY THE LAWS OF THE NARRATIVE THAT DRIVES OUR EXISTENCE IN THIS FICTIONAL WORLD...

...WE WILL MEET AGAIN.

WHA--

AND *THEN* YOU CAN ARREST ME!

HE'S COMING THIS WAY, LOOK OUT.

HUH?

CECIL! HE'S A *DOOMBOT!* ANY LUCK GHOST-HACKING HIM?

I CAN'T! HE'S GOT *MAGIC* PROTECTING HIM IN BITS AND PLACES OF HIS HARDWARE!

AAAAGRRGHH! OUT, SPIRIT!

YEAH, I GUESS DOCTOR DOOM *WOULD* DO THAT TO A ROBOT.

COMICS, MAN.

AHRM.

DON'T MOVE. YOU'RE UNDER ARREST.

WHAT?!

YEAH, *GWEN POOLE.* YOU'RE SHOOTING UP TIMES SQUARE. YOU'RE WANTED FOR A *BUNCH* OF OTHER CHARGES. YOU'RE UNDER ARREST!

I DON'T LIKE BEING SEPARATED FROM THE EYE FOR SO LONG. I'M LOSING MY CONNECTION WITH THE PLANES BEYOND...

AND I DON'T LIKE ZAT ZE PIG MADE MESS IN ZE CORNER AND NONE OF OUR CAPTORS SEE FIT TO CLEAN IT UP!

QWONK?

DO THEY KNOW WE HAD NOTHING TO DO WITH THE KILLING OF THE OTHER TEUTHIDANS? IT WAS JUST *GWEN* THAT DID THAT!*

GIVEN ZE VIGOR IN WHICH WE HAVE BEEN DETAINED, I DON'T THINK IT MATTERS.

*IT WASN'T, BUT NOBODY IN THIS ROOM KNOWS THAT. SEE ISSUE #1.

<THEY THINK WE'RE JUST WAITING AROUND FOR THEIR FORMER CLIENT TO COLLECT GWEN POOLE AND BRING HER BACK SO WE CAN DETAIN THE WHOLE GROUP.>**

<HA! SERIOUSLY? NONE OF THEM KNOW THEY'RE JUST *BAIT* FOR WHEN POOLE *DESTROYS* THAT LITTLE MAN AND COMES HERE TO SAVE HER FRIENDS?>

**TRANSLATED FROM SQUID ALIEN TALK.

THANK YOU VERY MUCH FOR YOUR BUSINESS! YOUR NEW LAPTOP HINGE SHOULD LAST LONGER THAN THE PREVIOUS.

HMFH, JUST LOOK AT THESE MUTANTS.

TERRIFYING.

I DO NOT UNDERSTAND. ARE THEY NOT DIFFERENT FROM HUMANITY MUCH LIKE I AM?

AND YOU DID NOT FEAR ME.

THAT'S NOT MY PROBLEM. THEY'VE GOT THESE SUPER-POWERS AND THEY JUST DO WHATEVER THEY WANT WITH THEM.

THEY ARE LIKE THAT SQUIRREL WOMAN WHO TRIED TO KILL YOU.

WHAT ARE GOOD NORMAL PEOPLE LIKE US SUPPOSED TO DO IN THE FACE OF THAT?

GOTTA KEEP UP SOMEHOW...

MBMBMLE... SPIDER-MAN WILL FINALLY SEE WHAT IT MEANS TO MESS WITH...

...THE TERRIBLE TINKERER!

VINCENT! WHERE ARE YOU? COME SEE THIS COOL THING I'M GOING TO DEFEAT SPIDER-MAN WITH!

...

VINCENT?!

"AND THAT IS WHEN I KNEW HOW AWFUL THIS WORLD COULD BE TO EVEN THE BEST OF FINE, ORDINARY PEOPLE. IT FRIGHTENS ME STILL. AND I MUST CHANGE IT."

"PAST DOCTOR DOOM. ALTERNATE FUTURE SQUIRREL GIRL. A NON-EVIL TINKERER BEFORE HIS FIRST ENCOUNTER WITH SPIDER-MAN?! HOW MANY DIFFERENT CHARACTERS IS YOUR ORIGIN TIED UP IN?! YIKES!"

LATER...

BEEP BEEP.

YES. LANGUAGE. YOU CLEARLY UNDERSTAND WHAT I'M SAYING, SO SOMEWHERE IN YOUR CIRCUITS THERE MUST BE A WAY TO OUTPUT...

DOOM!

I AM DOOM!

AH!

THAT CAN'T BE RIGHT.

SFOW

OH. HERE, I'LL JUST SWITCH THIS.

I APOLOGIZE. MY FRIEND. THANK YOU SO MUCH. OH, TO FINALLY EXPRESS MYSELF FULLY!

WOW! IT'S AS THOUGH YOU'VE BECOME FULLY HUMAN!

THANK YOU, PHINEAS.

I DON'T SUPPOSE YOU HAVE A NAME TUCKED IN THERE.

DOOM.

AH, AGAIN, THAT IS A VERY UNSETTLING THING TO KEEP SAYING.

VIIII...VOH... DOOM.

VIIII... VINCENT?

YES. I WILL BE VINCENT.

AS TIME WENT ON...

BEEP BEEP BEEP!

MY WORD! SOME SORT OF *ROBOTIC* MAN!

HELLO, FRIEND? DO YOU UNDERSTAND HUMAN LANGUAGE? IT IS VERY DIFFERENT THAN THE LANGUAGE OF PROGRAMMING, BUT YOU MAY!

BEEP?

A REACTION! INCREDIBLE! NOW, I'M SURE I'M GUILTY OF ANTHROPOMORPHIZING YOU, BUT YOU SEEM FRIGHTENED!

BEEP...

WELL, COME INSIDE! I'LL HIDE YOU FROM WHATEVER AWFUL MONSTROUS FORCE THAT'S PURSUING YOU.

COME ON! COME ON!

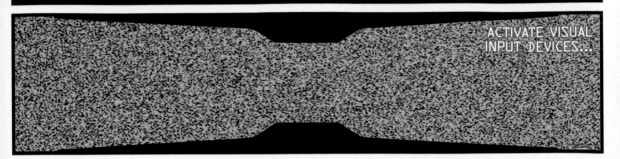

DECADES AGO...

...
......
SYSTEM STARTED

ACTIVATE VISUAL
INPUT DEVICES...

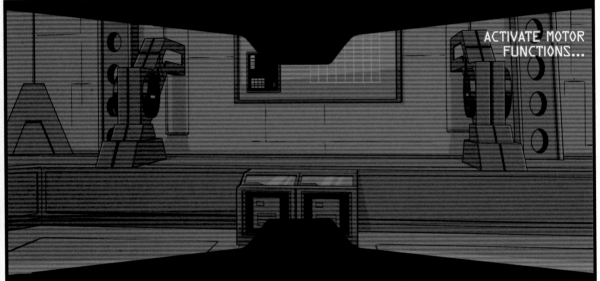

ACTIVATE MOTOR
FUNCTIONS...

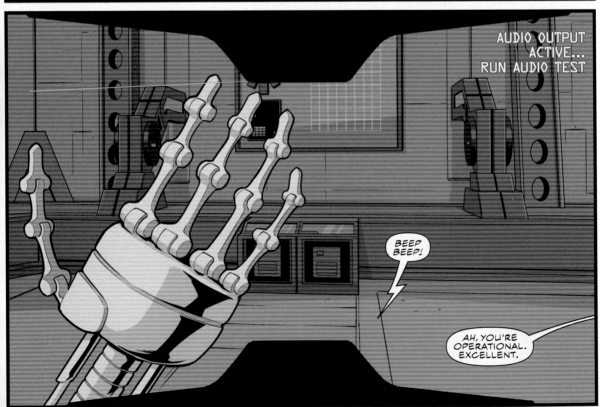

AUDIO OUTPUT
ACTIVE...
RUN AUDIO TEST

BEEP BEEP!

AH, YOU'RE
OPERATIONAL.
EXCELLENT.

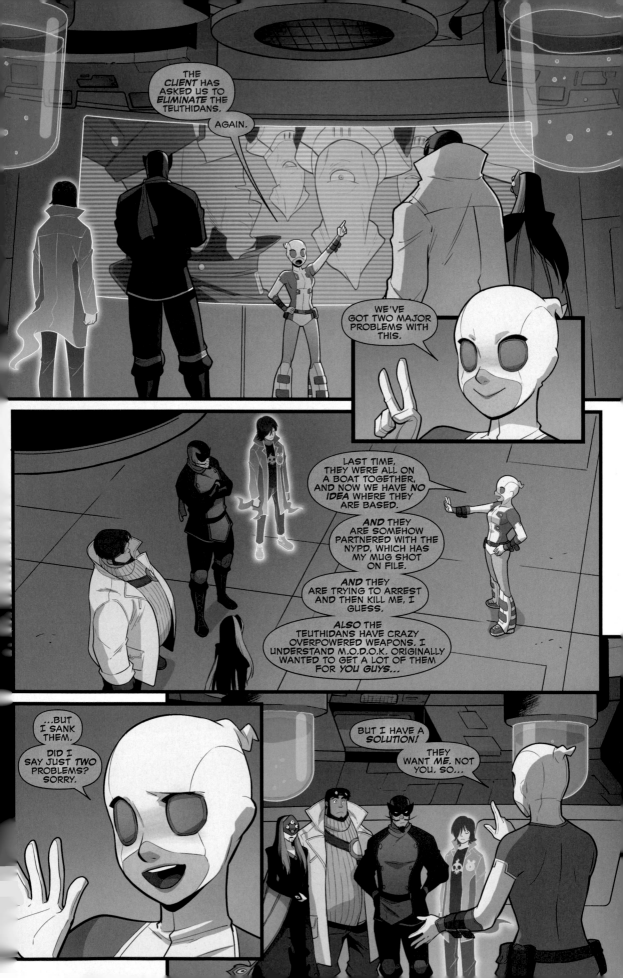

NOTHING. BUT LISTEN. DON'T WORRY. I'VE GOT A PLAN-- UH, YOUR PHONE?

BZZT

GOT AN, UH...OLD MEDICAL BILL.

UNKNOWN

BZZT BZZT

YOU? THE *PARTY HEALER*?

HEH.

THE "PARTY HEALER" WAS ONCE A STUDENT WHO HAD TO STAY IN A HOSPITAL FOR A WHILE...

...WITHOUT INSURANCE.

WOOF.

WELL, OUR CLIENT'S GOT A GREAT JOB FOR, AND I QUOTE...

..."A DUMP TRUCK FULL OF MONEY"...

...AND I KNOW HOW TO PULL IT OFF. MEET ON THE... BRIDGE?

I GUESS THAT MAIN ROOM IS THE BRIDGE.

WOW. GWEN?

YEAH?

ARE YOU THE LEADER OF M.O.D.O.K. TEAM NOW?

UH...

HEE HEE!

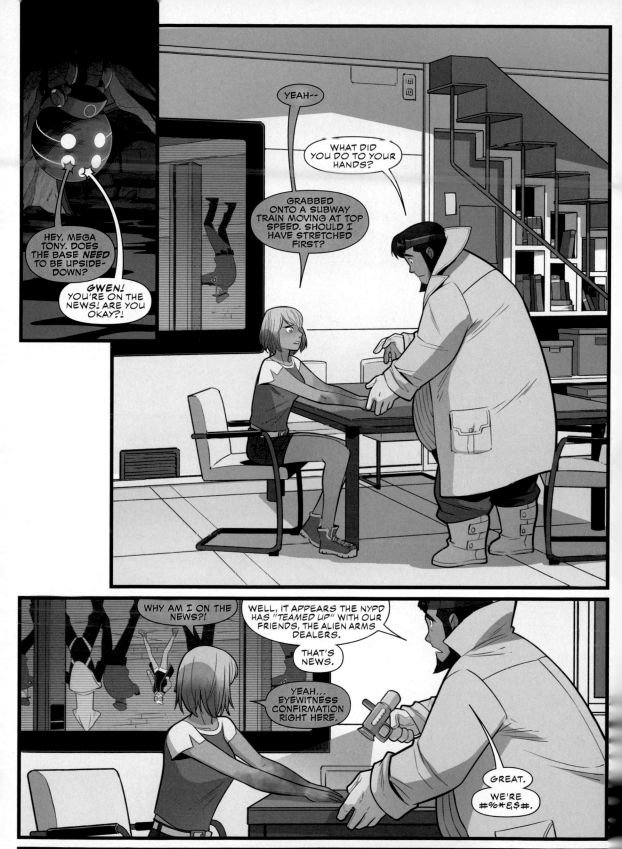

HEY, MEGA TONY. DOES THE BASE *NEED* TO BE UPSIDE-DOWN?

GWEN! YOU'RE ON THE NEWS! ARE YOU OKAY?!

YEAH--

WHAT DID YOU DO TO YOUR HANDS?

GRABBED ONTO A SUBWAY TRAIN MOVING AT TOP SPEED. SHOULD I HAVE STRETCHED FIRST?

WHY AM I ON THE NEWS?!

WELL, IT APPEARS THE NYPD HAS "TEAMED UP" WITH OUR FRIENDS, THE ALIEN ARMS DEALERS.

THAT'S NEWS.

YEAH... EYEWITNESS CONFIRMATION RIGHT HERE.

GREAT. WE'RE #%*&$#.

MEGA TONY. THERE IS *NO* WAY THEY ARE GOING TO PRINT WHAT YOU JUST SAID!

WHAT?

SO...WIPE OUT A BATTALION OF SUPER-ADVANCED ALIENS. WASN'T TOO LONG AGO I'D FEEL PRETTY CONFIDENT ABOUT THAT!

IT'S NOT LIKE I'VE BEEN WRONG ABOUT ALL THIS STUFF. SURE, CECIL *DIED* BECAUSE I TOOK CREDIT FOR KILLING THE ALIENS, BUT THEN HE CAME BACK WITH *GHOST POWERS.*

WHY DOESN'T HE JUST *ENJOY* THAT?

IT'S NOT LIKE HE'S GOT SWAYZE GHOST PROBLEMS, LIKE PEOPLE CAN'T SEE HIM OR WHATEVER.

...

I WONDER IF SPIDER-MAN'S STILL MAD AT ME FOR TRYING TO SHOOT THAT GUY--*STOP IT, GWEN.*

WHEN IS THIS *TRAIN* GOING TO GET HERE? I AM GETTING MOROSE.

UH-OH.

T-CHNKT

HEH, UH, "SQUID ALIEN FREAK" IS A *COMPLIMENT* HERE.

GOOD.

≈SIGH≈

CAPTAIN?

KNOCK KNOCK

YES, LIEUTENANT?

NO LEAD ON WHERE THE M.O.D.O.K. BASE IS CURRENTLY. PROBABLY ON THE RUN FROM THOSE SQUID ALIEN FREAKS THAT WERE ATTACKING THEM.

THE TEUTHIDANS.

THAT WHAT THEY'RE CALLED? WHATEVER.

YES, THANK YOU, CAPTAIN. DISMISSED.

CECIL! YOU'RE BACK! WHERE IS GWEN?!

NEVER MIND. STUPID QUESTION. YOU CAN PASS THROUGH WALLS AND SHE CAN'T. SHE'S TAKING THE ELEVATOR.

OH! OKAY, THAT'S GOOD. THAT'S PROBABLY GOOD.

NO, SHE'S STILL AT THE MEETING WITH OUR CLIENT.

AHA! GHOST FRIEND. MAY I ASK YOU A QUESTION?

UH, SURE?

I HAVE STUDIED THE ARCANA. I HAVE SEEN THE PLANES. I...

...HAVE HARMED MYSELF IN THE PURSUIT OF KNOWLEDGE BEYOND THIS REALM.

BUT THERE IS ONE STATE I CANNOT PIERCE.

TELL ME, WHAT IS THERE AFTER DEATH?

WHOA! AH...

...I DON'T REMEMBER ANYTHING. IT WAS LIKE SLEEPING.

SO, THERE IS NOTHING.

SORRY...

HA HA!

I THOUGHT THE REALMS BEYOND CORPOREAL LIFE WERE SIMPLY A SEA OF INSANITY, WHERE ANCIENT BEINGS TELL SECRET PLOTS IN A LANGUAGE THAT WOULD TURN US TO JELLY SHOULD IT CROSS OUR EARDRUMS...

BUT YOU DIDN'T SEE THAT! SERIOUSLY, BIG RELIEF. ADDS A LOT TO MY RESEARCH.

WAIT, WHAT? YOU MEAN CECIL THE FRIENDLY GHOST OVER HERE? HE'S TOTALLY COOL.

HE'S WITH ME.

GWEN, IT'S FINE. I GUESS I SHOULD GET USED TO THIS TREATMENT...

...FOR THE REST OF ETERNITY.

YOU MADE IT HERE SAFE. YOU DIDN'T NEED ANY "GHOST HACKS." I'LL SEE YOU BACK AT BASE.

THANK YOU FOR RESPECTING MY WISHES, *WRAITH.* I WISH YOU REST IN PEACE SOON.

THANKS?

WHAT WAS *THAT* ABOUT?

IT IS ABOUT ONE VALUE I HOLD ABOVE ALL ELSE.

THE PEACE OF THE MUNDANE.

NO, GWEN. I DO NOT SENSE DRACULA.

I DON'T KNOW IF I COULD SENSE DRACULA.

LISTEN, I DON'T EVEN THINK I SHOULD BE HERE RIGHT NOW.

OH, NO? WHAT ELSE YOU GOT GOING ON? YOU'RE DEAD! HA H--

TOO SOON. TOTALLY.

UH.

WE ALL HAVE OUR OWN WAYS OF GRIEVING.

HAVE I SAID I'M GLAD YOU'RE BACK? I'M SO GLAD.

YEAH! YOU HAVE! AND, I GUESS, ME TOO?

BUT, LIKE, THIS IS WEIRD.

I GET IT, MAN.

I DON'T THINK YOU DO. IT-- --IS WEIRD.

I MEAN, MY FAMILY BACK IN WEST VIRGINIA, THEY STILL THINK I'M MISSING. THEY PROBABLY THINK I'M DEAD.

WELL--

NO.

HELLO? IT'S GWEN POOLE? I ASSUME YOU'RE EXPECTING ME?

...OR YOUR DOORBELL HAS A *CONSIDERABLE* SECURITY FLAW?

HMM...

LET'S SEE, LET'S SEE. WE'VE NEVER SEEN THE *HOST* ON THE VIDEO CALLS. WE'RE BASICALLY IN THE MIDDLE OF *NOWHERE, NEW YORK*. SPOOKY DOOR. EMPTY HOUSE. *FINE* DECORATIONS.

IT'S *DRACULA.* I'M CALLING IT. WE'RE MEETING *DRACULA.*

WHAT DO YOU SAY, CECIL?

DO YOUR *GHOST* SENSES PICK UP ANYTHING ON THE *KING OF THE VAMPIRES?*

...

CECIL. STOP BEING INVISIBLE.

DO YOU KNOW THIS BECAUSE...

...COMIC BOOKS?

THEY ARE RACIST, BATROC. THEY ARE OUR ENEMY, AND THEY ARE ALIENS, AND THEY ARE RACIST.

UH, MAYBE? I DON'T KNOW?

I HAVE NEVER HEARD OF THESE ALIENS.

DROP YOUR WEAPONS! DROP THE PIG!

SO, THEY WERE PROBABLY MADE UP *SPECIFICALLY* FOR ME TO MESS WITH, AND I THINK THIS IS A GOOD WAY TO MESS WITH THEM.

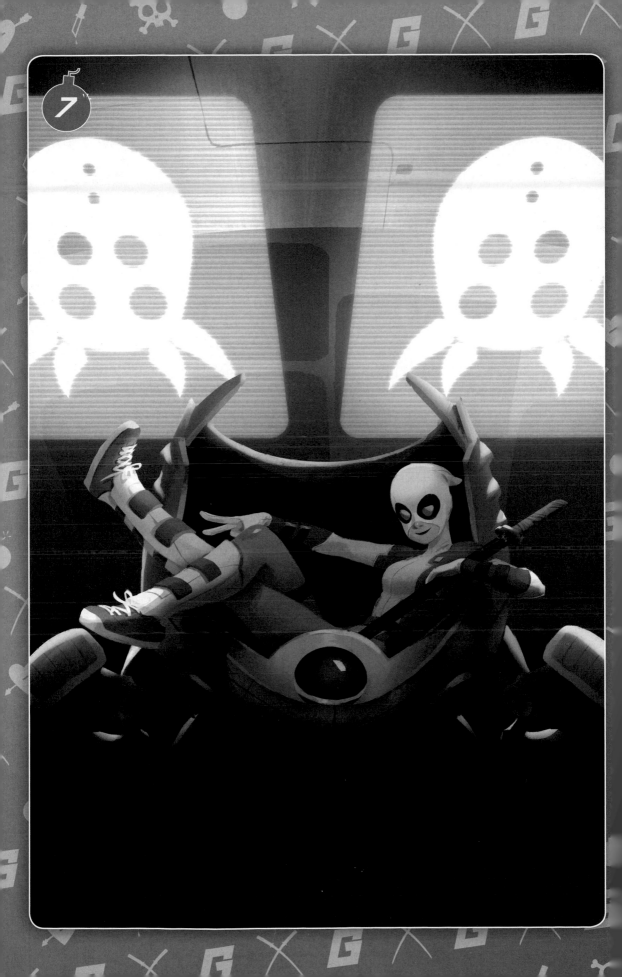

THANKS, BATROC.

GWEN! WHAT HAPPENED?!

WHERE WERE YOU?

I MET SPIDER-MAN.

IT DIDN'T GO GREAT.

AT LEAST YOU'RE STILL ALIVE.

HEY, THAT'S NOT FAIR.

WAIT, I KILLED THEM!

TELL HIM I--

NOT THESE ONES.

UGH, I'LL GET BACK ON WORKING UP A DEFENSE AGAINST THE TEUTHIDANS.

I'LL TRY TO SET UP A NEW MEETING WITH THE CLIENT SO HE WON'T FIRE US.

--GOT EXCITED TO RUN OFF WITH SPIDER-MAN AND ABANDONED US? NO, I'LL MAKE SOMETHING UP, DO NOT WORRY.

I...

...THIS ISN'T FUN.

DUDE... ...YOU'RE SUPPOSED TO PULL PUNCHES AGAINST *NORMALS*...

I DID.

WAIT, WHAT ARE YOU DOING?

I'M LEAVING YOU FOR THE POLICE.

WHAT?! NO!

I'LL, UH...I'LL TELL EVERYONE WHO YOU ARE!

YEAH, I'M GETTING READY FOR THAT.

BECAUSE I'M NOT LETTING A MURDERER LOOSE.

I WON'T TELL.

YEAH, I HOPE NOT.

I'M GOING TO MAKE SURE DAMIAN DOESN'T HAVE ANYTHING WORSE THAN A CONCUSSION AND MAKE SURE HE DOESN'T *BOMB* ANY MORE SCHOOLS.

I HOPE YOU GET BETTER.

I'M NOT--

--I'M NOT CRAZY, SPIDER-MAN.

...SHE'S THE ONE THAT SHOT UP THAT BANK AND STOLE McGINTY'S CRUISER.

SHE PROBABLY KILLED HIM, TOO. HE'S DISAPPEARED.*

*SEE MY FIRST ISSUE, I GUESS. WHATEVER. -GWEN

I'D LIKE TO CALL MY LAWYER, PLEASE.

MILES!

HONEY, ARE YOU OKAY?

WHAT? YES. WHY?

THEY FOUND THE SCHOOL BOMBER. THERE WAS A SHOOTING. THEY THINK SPIDER-MAN OR THIS PINK PERSON DID IT.

I DOUBT IT WAS SPIDER-MAN, MOM.

...

THAT'S GOOD.

PINK GHOST CAUGHT

NOT VERY DISCREET AT ALL. DISAPPOINTING.

YOU ALMOST KILLED HIM! WHY?! WHY?!

HE BLEW UP YOUR SCHOOL, DUDE! I WAS *TRYING* TO SAVE YOU A TON OF HASSLE!

HASSLE?! NOT *KILLING* PEOPLE ISN'T ABOUT CONVENIENCE!

HE WASN'T IMPORTANT! HE WAS A PLOT DEVICE! A B-STORY!

WHAT ARE YOU *SAYING?!*

SOMEBODY SAID "OH, REMEMBER THAT KID WHO WAS GOING TO BOMB THE SCHOOL IN THE *ULTIMATE* UNIVERSE? HE CAN DO IT IN THE *MAIN* ONE NOW!"

OH, GOD...

YOU'RE IN A *COMIC BOOK*, MILES!

YOU'RE... YOU'RE JUST A *CRAZY* PERSON.

NO. I'M THE BABY PUNISHER TO YOUR BABY SPIDER-MAN.

NO...
NO...
NO...

OH, CHILL OUT, LADY. YOUR *SUPER VILLAIN* IN *THE MAKING* IS TOTALLY *FINE,* NO THANKS TO *SPIDER-MAN* HERE!

SEE YOU NEVER!

WHAT DID YOU DO TO MY SON?!

WHY DID SPIDER-MAN *BREAK* INTO MY *HOUSE* TO *HURT* MY SON?!

I *SAVED* HIS LIFE! HE JUST HIT HIS HEAD!

≳SOB≲

COME ON, SPIDEY! WE'LL FIGURE OUT HOW TO TAKE HIM OUT ANOTHER DAY!

AAAAAH!

WHY'D YOU DO IT, MAN?

SPIDER-MAN?

YOU BOMBED A CLASSROOM BECAUSE OF "SPIDER-MAN"? I DON'T BUY THAT.

BOOM

HOW DID YOU FIND ME?

CLASS DIRECTORY.

SPIDER-SENSE.

WELL, I WAS COMPLETELY JUSTIFIED IN MY ACTIONS.

UH-HUH.

SEE, THE LOTTERY SCHOOL SYSTEM IS A SYMBOL OF INEQUALITY.

YEAH, I SEE THAT.

OKAY, SO... YEAH. LIKE, THE SYSTEM IS, UH, UNJUST AND... THAT'S IT.

I WANTED TO DESTROY IT.

THIS IS THE FIRST TIME I'VE SAID IT OUT LOUD.

SO, DO YOU NEED TO BE KNOCKED OUT BEFORE I HAND YOU OVER TO THE COPS OR...

NO! DON'T!

THUNK

HUH?

BING BONG

BING BONG

MOM! THE DOOR!

I'M IN THE BATHROOM!

≶GRUMBLE≶

YEAH?

HELLO?

THE WHAT?

WHY IS *THAT GUY* HERE?!

BECAUSE THE *WRITER* DIDN'T WANT TO DROP THE "SCHOOL BOMBER" STORYLINE THAT HE WAS SETTING UP BEFORE *SECRET WARS!*

WHAT DO YOU MEAN, "WRITER"? "ULTIMATE UNIVERSE"?

AH...

...OKAY, I'LL TELL YOU THE TRUTH. I DON'T HAVE DEAD WATCHER POWERS.

I'M FROM ANOTHER WORLD, TOO.

AND...

TRUTH OR NOT, TRY TO KEEP SPIDER-MAN FROM THINKING YOU'RE CRAZY! NOTHING ABOUT COMIC BOOKS.

WE CAN SEE WHAT HAPPENS IN THIS UNIVERSE THERE. AND THERE ARE, *UH...*WRITERS? LIKE UNIVERSE ARCHITECTS?

TRUST ME.

YOU DON'T MAKE THAT EASY.

DO YOU REMEMBER ONE TIME YOU WERE SNEAKING BACK INTO SCHOOL, AND YOU RAN INTO THAT GUY IN THE ABANDONED ART ROOM?

OH! YEAH, I FORGOT ABOUT THAT.

OKAY, SO YOU DIDN'T SEE IT, BUT HE WAS TOTALLY UP TO SOMETHING. LET ME ASK YOU...

...IS HE IN ANY OF YOUR CLASSES NOW?

UH...

YEAH! HIS NAME'S DAMIAN! WE HAVE ENGLISH LIT TOGETHER.

BOOM! THERE IT IS!

I DON'T THINK I FOLLOW...

ONLY YOU AND YOUR FAMILY AND OTHER IMPORTANT CHARACTERS MADE IT HERE FROM THE ULTIMATE UNIVERSE!

SO THIS IS *SPIDER-MAN'S* ROOM.

STOP SAYING THAT!

SORRY.

LISTEN, I APPRECIATE YOU COMING OUT OF NOWHERE AND WANTING TO HELP, BUT GIVEN HOW YOU HANDLED THE BOMBING AT THE SCHOOL...

‡HACK‡ ‡HACK‡ ‡HACK‡ ‡AACGHH!‡

...MAYBE WE PART WAYS FOR NOW?

DUDE, I CAN TOTALLY HELP! I, LIKE, KNOW *SECRET* STUFF.

YEAH, YOUR MULTIPLE INDISCRETIONS WITH MY SECRET IDENTITY HAVE PROVED THAT.

HM...DO YOU REMEMBER WHAT YOUR LIFE WAS LIKE IN YOUR OLD UNIVERSE?

OLD UNIVERSE? WHAT?

YOU KNOW, LIKE WHEN YOUR MOM WAS DEAD?

UH, SHE LOOKS *PRETTY ALIVE* TO ME.

EXACTLY. SHE MADE IT *HERE*, BECAUSE SHE'S IMPORTANT.

GWEN--

QUIET! I'M ON A ROLL!

MILES, THAT DUDE DOESN'T LIKE YOOOOU!

WELL, WHATEVER THAT GUY WAS PLANNING, *SECRET WARS* IS PROBABLY GOING TO TOTALLY MESS IT UP...

WHAT WITH THE UNIVERSES GETTING ALL BLOWN UP AND--

RRRUUMMMBBLLEE

HUH?

MERCI, MONSIEUR. IF WE HEAR ANYTHING WE'LL LET YOU KNOW.

GWEN NEVER MADE IT TO ZE MEETING. SHE'S NOT ANSWERING HER PHONE.

INCOMING CALL FROM OUTER SPACE

OH, NO...

A CALL FROM SPACE! IT'S M.O.D.O.K.! HE FOUND A PHONE IN SPACE!

QUIET, TONY. YOU'VE DONE NOTHING WRONG.

BONJOUR! THIS IS M.O.D.O.K. TEAM.

WHERE ZE HELL ARE YOU, GWEN?

OBVIOUSLY YOU'LL BE HOME FROM SCHOOL UNTIL EVERYTHING'S SAFE AGAIN. BUT GWEN SAYS YOU'VE GOT A TEAM ASSIGNMENT?

YEAH, WE'VE GOT A *BIG* PROJECT WE NEED TO WORK ON TOGETHER.

THE MYSTERIOUS BOMBING! WE GOTTA SOLVE IT! IT'S A SPIDER-MAN TEAM-UP! THIS IS GREAT!

WE DO.

OKAY, WELL KEEP YOUR DOOR OPEN. NO OFFENSE, GWEN.

...

OKAY.

YOU'RE A STRONG WOMAN AND I RESPECT YOU!

LATER...
THE MORALES HOUSE.

MILES! I HEARD ABOUT SCHOOL! I'M SO GLAD YOU'RE OKAY! WHERE WERE YOU?!

OH, UH, I HAD TO GIVE A STATEMENT, AND GOT HELD UP.

WELL, YOUR FRIEND GWEN FROM SCHOOL GOT OUT OKAY, TOO.

WAIT, GWEN?

FACE IT, TIGER! YOU JUST GOT A STUDY BUDDY!

WHAT?

SINCE WHEN DO PEOPLE CALL YOU "TIGER"?

THEY DON'T.

IT'S A...

...REFERENCE.

TP
TP
TP

LATE.

I'LL HAVE TO DO SOMETHING ABOUT IT.

CLICK

NEXT ON JUDGE JACLYN'S COURT!

Judge Jaclyn

LISTEN, YOU LITTLE TURKEY, DON'T POOP IN MY CAPPUCCINO AND CALL IT BISCOTTI!

A NEW EPISODE. EXCELLENT. I WILL...

...FOR NOW.

THIS WAS THE CLASS I WAS LATE TO...

WHERE'S GANKE?! OH, NO...

HEY! HEY, ARE YOU OKAY?!

SPIDER-MAN...

≥COUGH≤ ≥COUGH≤...HRK HOO BOY.

≥COUGH≤ NEED... FLAME WARRIOR VARIANT COSTUME.

AH, I SHOULDN'T HAVE BROUGHT YOU IN HERE!

NO! I'M A SUPER-FRIEND! I'M HELPING! ≥HACK≤ ≥COUGH≤

HELP LIKE THIS. HERE. HOLD TIGHT.

THWIP

SO, LIKE JUST COMFORTING HUGS OR--

YOU ABSOLUTELY CANNOT TELL ANYBODY.

I DEFINITELY WON'T.

I WOULD LOVE TO SIT DOWN AND TALK ALL ABOUT WATCHERS, AND DANGEROUS KNOWLEDGE OR WHATEVER, BUT I'M ALREADY LATE FOR CLASS AND--

OH, MY GOD. I GOTTA GET IN THERE.

WORD UP.

HOW WE DOING THIS?

THUNK

AWESOOOOOOME!

MEANWHILE...

LITTLE SPECTRE
IN A BIG CITY:

I CAN'T
OPEN THIS
BOOK!

AH! TRAIN! THWIPS! SPIDER-MAN! LOVE YOU! AH!

WHO ARE YOU? HOW DO YOU KNOW WHO I AM?!

≶GULP≷

I REALLY DON'T NEED HIM THINKING I'M CRAZY RIGHT NOW.

I'M A NORMAL GIRL WHO WAS GIFTED WITH SECRET KNOWLEDGE FROM A DYING WATCHER.

DAMN. OKAY.

FUNNY HOW THAT WAS MORE PLAUSIBLE.

I HAVE NO INTENTION OF SPOILING YOUR SECRET IDENTITY.

I WAS JUST EXCITED TO MEET A REAL SPIDER-MAN.

SO, WHAT, YOU KNOW MY WHOLE LIFE HISTORY?

THE INTERESTING PARTS!

WHAT AM I SUPPOSED TO DO ABOUT YOU?

WELL, I KNOW YOU DON'T KILL. SO, HELP ME HOP THIS NEXT TRAIN?

AAAAH, LATE AGAAAAIN.

CAN'T GO SWINGING ACROSS TOWN WITH MY FACE HALF EXPOSED THOUGH.

NOT UNTIL PEOPLE GET OVER THIS WHOLE *CAMERAS-ON-PHONES* FAD...

WAITWAITWAITWAIT *YESSSS!*

PHEW

!!!

HOPE THAT DOESN'T SCAR--

CRAP, I AM EXPOSED.

SORRY ABOUT YOUR TRUCK, *TOM.* WHOEVER YOU ARE. OR WHATEVER SERVICE IT IS YOU DO WITH THIS TRUCK.

OH. MONSTERS.

CAN'T ARREST MONSTERS.

≥SIGH≤

HEY, YOU SEE WHAT THE DEAL WAS WITH THESE THINGS?

I SAW *SPIDER-MAN* TAKE THEM OUT! HE WAS GREAT, AND THEN HE WENT IN THE COMPLETE OPPOSITE DIRECTION AS ME!

THUNK

UH... WHO IS OUR NEW REPRESENTATIVE?

DO WE EVEN HAVE TO WORK HERE ANYMORE?

YEAH, I LIKE YOU ALL AND EVERYTHING, BUT THIS HAS BEEN KIND OF A SIDE QUEST FOR ME, I THINK. I'D RATHER JUST BOUNCE AND GO BACK TO FREELANCING.

WE HAVE ALL JUST INHERITED A *MASSIVE MOBILE FORTRESS*, AND M.O.D.O.K.'S EMPLOYER STILL WANTS TO *WORK WITH US.*

WE ARE *ALL* MERCENARIES, EVEN THE *CUDDLIEST* OF US.

WE WON'T DO BETTER ON OUR OWN. LET US KEEP OUR ADVANTAGES.

HEE.

BATROC IS RIGHT! M.O.D.O.K. WILL SURELY RETURN TO KILL US!

THAT IS NOT WHAT I SAID.

BATROC IS RIGHT! WE SHOULD STICK TOGETHER AND PREPARE TO DEFEND OURSELVES AGAINST M.O.D.O.K.'S RETURN!

I'M NOT--≥SIGH≤ YES. THAT'S RIGHT.

SO WHO...

GWEN WILL GO.

WHAT? *YOU'RE* THE ADULT! *YOU* SHOULD GO!

YOU'VE WON ME OVER, GWEN. YOU HAVE NO SUPER-POWERS, NO EXTRAORDINARY SKILLS, BUT YOU *DEFEATED M.O.D.O.K.* YOU HAVE *SOMETHING.*

I THINK I'M IN A COMIC THAT JUST GOT RENEWED AND I CAN'T DIE YET IS WHAT HAPPENED.

WE CAN CHOOSE TO DISAGREE ON ZE SOURCE OF YOUR *JE NE SAIS QUOI.*

BUT I BELIEVE IN YOU.

AW, GEEZ. MR. *THE LEAPER...*

REMEMBER. HE SAID *DISCREET.*

THAT MEANS *PLAIN CLOTHES,* AND *PUBLIC TRANSPORTATION.* HERE'S A METRO CARD.

GWEN, I SAID *THE CLIENT* IS ON THE PHONE FOR YOU.

OH, *SORRY!* I *JUST* STOPPED M.O.D.O.K. FROM KILLING ME *SIXTY SECONDS AGO* AND I WANTED SOME *FRESH AIR* AND I DIDN'T REALIZE WE *DIDN'T* HAVE VOICEMAIL SET UP IN THIS THING.

TELL HIM I'LL CALL HIM *BACK!*

WHAT IS IT?

WHY DON'T YOU FIND THE PERSON WHO'S BEEN TELLING M.O.D.O.K. WHAT TO DO EVEN *SCARIER* THAN M.O.D.O.K.?

HA HA...

ULP.

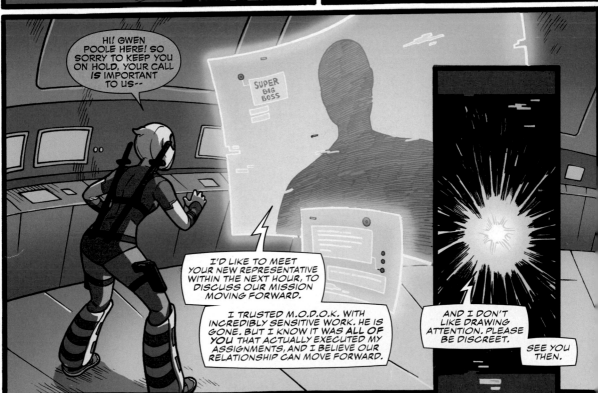

HI! GWEN POOLE HERE! SO SORRY TO KEEP YOU ON HOLD, YOUR CALL *IS* IMPORTANT TO US--

SUPER BIG BOSS

I'D LIKE TO MEET YOUR NEW REPRESENTATIVE WITHIN THE NEXT HOUR, TO DISCUSS OUR MISSION MOVING FORWARD.

I TRUSTED M.O.D.O.K. WITH INCREDIBLY SENSITIVE WORK. HE IS GONE. BUT I KNOW IT WAS *ALL OF YOU* THAT ACTUALLY EXECUTED MY ASSIGNMENTS, AND I BELIEVE OUR RELATIONSHIP CAN MOVE FORWARD.

AND I DON'T LIKE DRAWING ATTENTION. PLEASE BE DISCREET.

SEE YOU THEN.

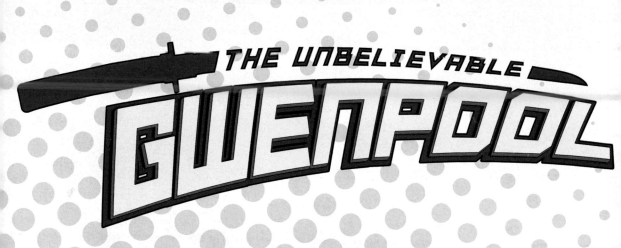

THE UNBELIEVABLE GWENPOOL

TRUE BELIEVERS, PREPARE TO HAVE YOUR MARVEL-OUS MINDS BLOWN TO PLUTO AND BACK!

GUESS WHO MADE IT THROUGH HER FIRST ARC ALMOST ENTIRELY UNSCATHED (PLUS OR MINUS ONE OR TWO FRIENDS, SOME STACKS OF CASH AND JUST A LI'L BIT OF THE OL' DIGNITY)? NONE OTHER THAN YOUR GIRL, *GWEN POOLE!*

I USED TO BE YOUR BASIC FANGIRL BLOWING HER PAYCHECK ON COMICS AND STATUES, BUT NOW I'M OUT THERE THROWING HAMMERS WITH THOR AND SWINGING INTO THE SUNSET WITH SPIDER-MAN--YOU KNOW, LIVING THE DREAM.

LITERALLY. I HAVE A RECURRING DREAM WHERE MILES MORALES AND I ARE BROS AND WE FIGHT DINOSAURS IN THE SAVAGE LAND.

I'LL EXPLAIN MORE IN, LIKE...A PAGE, BUT BELIEVE ME WHEN I SAY I AM KILLING IT!

THE HATERS ARE CRYING, AND YOU CAN BET I'M ONLY JUST GETTING STARTED.